SCIENCE CREATIONS
PRESENTS

to

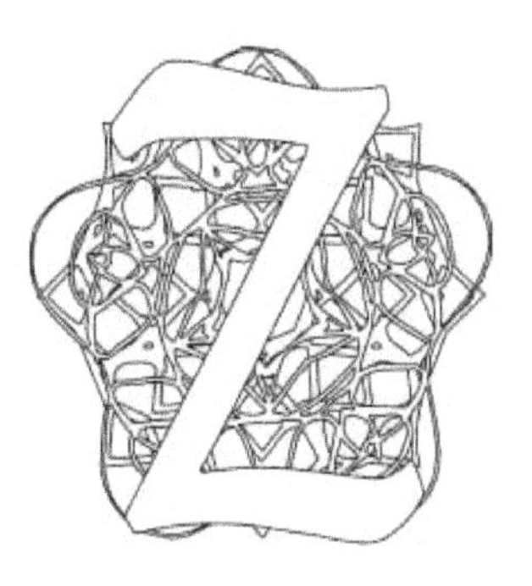

Herbs and Spices
Coloring Book

Inspired by Gloria Zarinah Saleem Muhammad
Written By Serena Muhammad
Illustrated By Jamil Salih

A to Z Herbs and Spices

Published by DEEP ROOTS BOOKS

Illustrations by Jamil Salih
Cover and interior designed by Ruqayyah K. Muhammad

This book is available from
ScienceCreations.com
Amazon.com
and at selected bookstores worldwide.

For permission requests, or for further ordering information, contact the publisher at: **info@deeprootsbooks.com**
Visit **DeepRootsBooks.com** for more information.

ISBN 978-0-620-91514-4

Published 21 February 2021
Printed in the United States of America

This Coloring Book Belongs To:

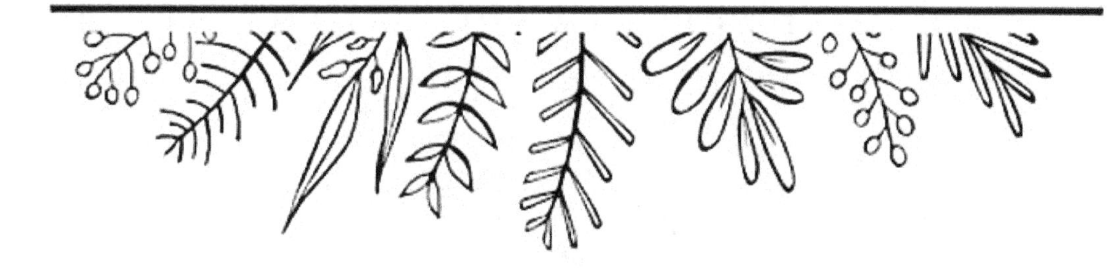

The pages of this book may be colored with crayons, colored pencils, felt-tip markers, paints, etc. We have left the reverse pages of each coloring page blank to help prevent bleed-through. You may want to insert a blank sheet of paper behind the page you are coloring to further prevent bleed-through.

We hope you enjoy coloring in this book as much as we enjoyed creating it!

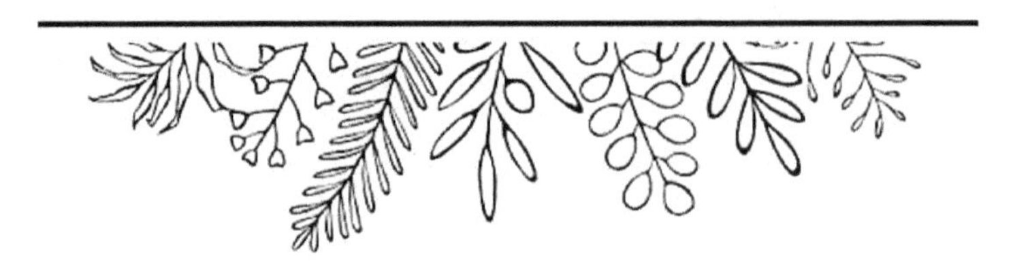

This coloring book is dedicated to my mother

Gloria Zarinah Saleem Muhammad

who inspired this project to teach children
and adults to use nature (Creation) to learn
from the many health benefits that are found
in plants. She practiced and promoted natural
healing remedies. May her many lessons be
helpful to other parents as they teach their
children about the beauty and benefits
of the Creation found around us.

Love Daughter #5 ,

Serena ❁

A is for Aloe Vera
Aloe Vera is used to treat cuts and burns.

B is for Basil,
Black Pepper,
and Black Seed
If you have an insect bite, try using Basil.
Black Pepper is good for brain power.
Black Seed has many benefits; its oil might help if you have asthma.

C is for Cloves and Cinnamon

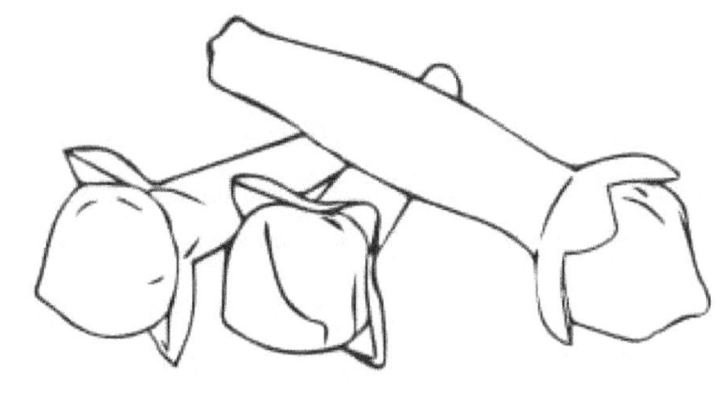

If you have a toothache, try cloves.

If your stomach hurts, try drinking tea with Cinnamon.

D is for Dandelion
Dandelion tea helps with bloating and gas.

E is for Eucalyptus

For congestion and bad coughs, Eucalyptus may help.

F is for Fennel
and Frankincense
Fennel can be used to flavor salads
and can be taken by new mommies to help them
make milk for their babies.
Frankincense smells good and can
help us feel calm.

G is for Garlic
and Ginger
Garlic is great to flavor food and
helps us stay healthy.
If your stomach hurts,
try putting Ginger in your tea.

H is for
Hawthorne Berry
and Hibiscus
Hawthorne Berry is good for your heart.
Hibiscus is a beautiful flower that
can help our muscles relax.

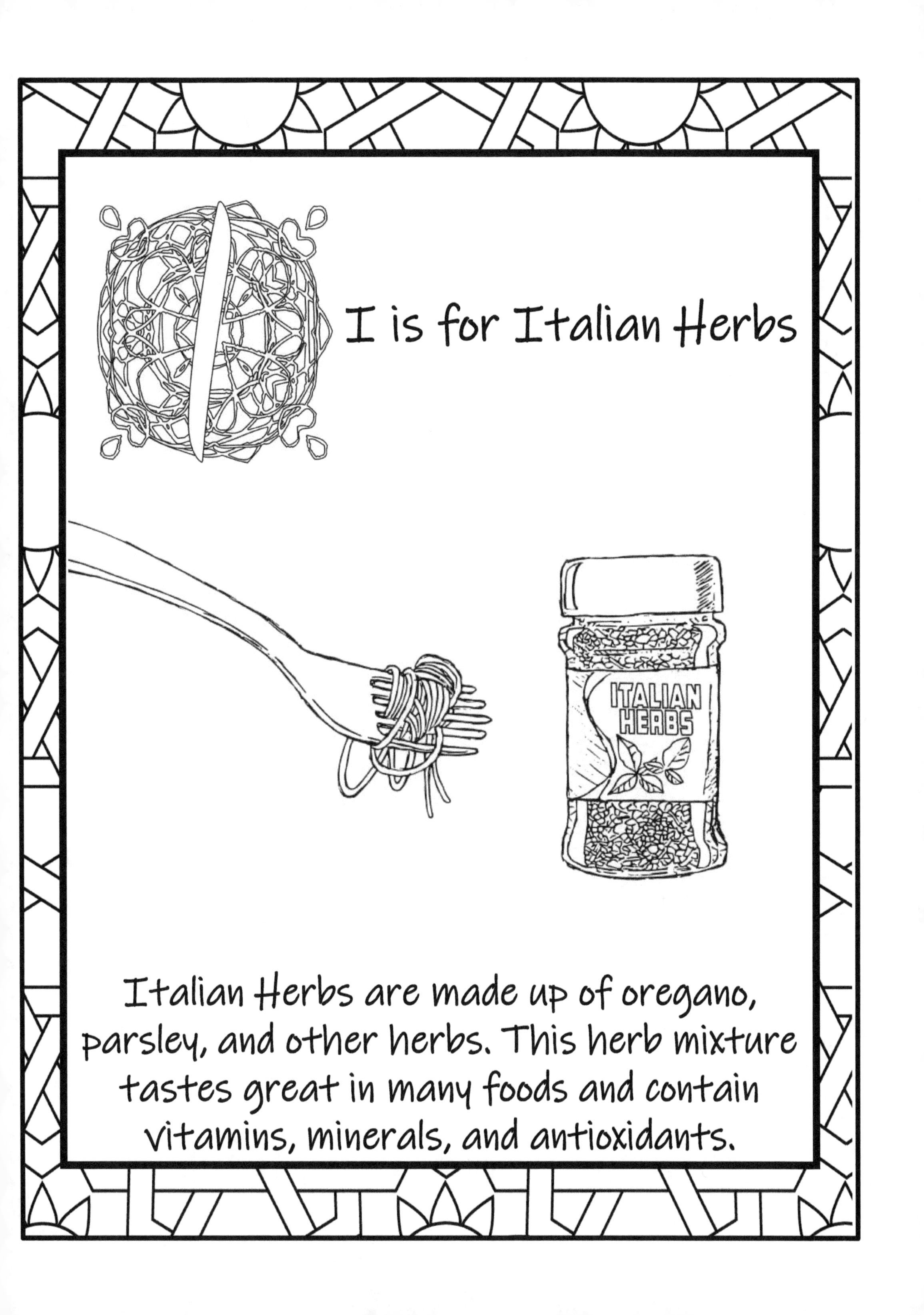

I is for Italian Herbs

Italian Herbs are made up of oregano, parsley, and other herbs. This herb mixture tastes great in many foods and contain vitamins, minerals, and antioxidants.

J is for Juniper Berries
Juniper Berries can help with healing wounds.

K is for Kombucha

Kombucha is made from green or black tea. It has probiotics in it which helps with digestion.

L is for Lavender
Lavender is a purple flower that can help
with stress and headaches.

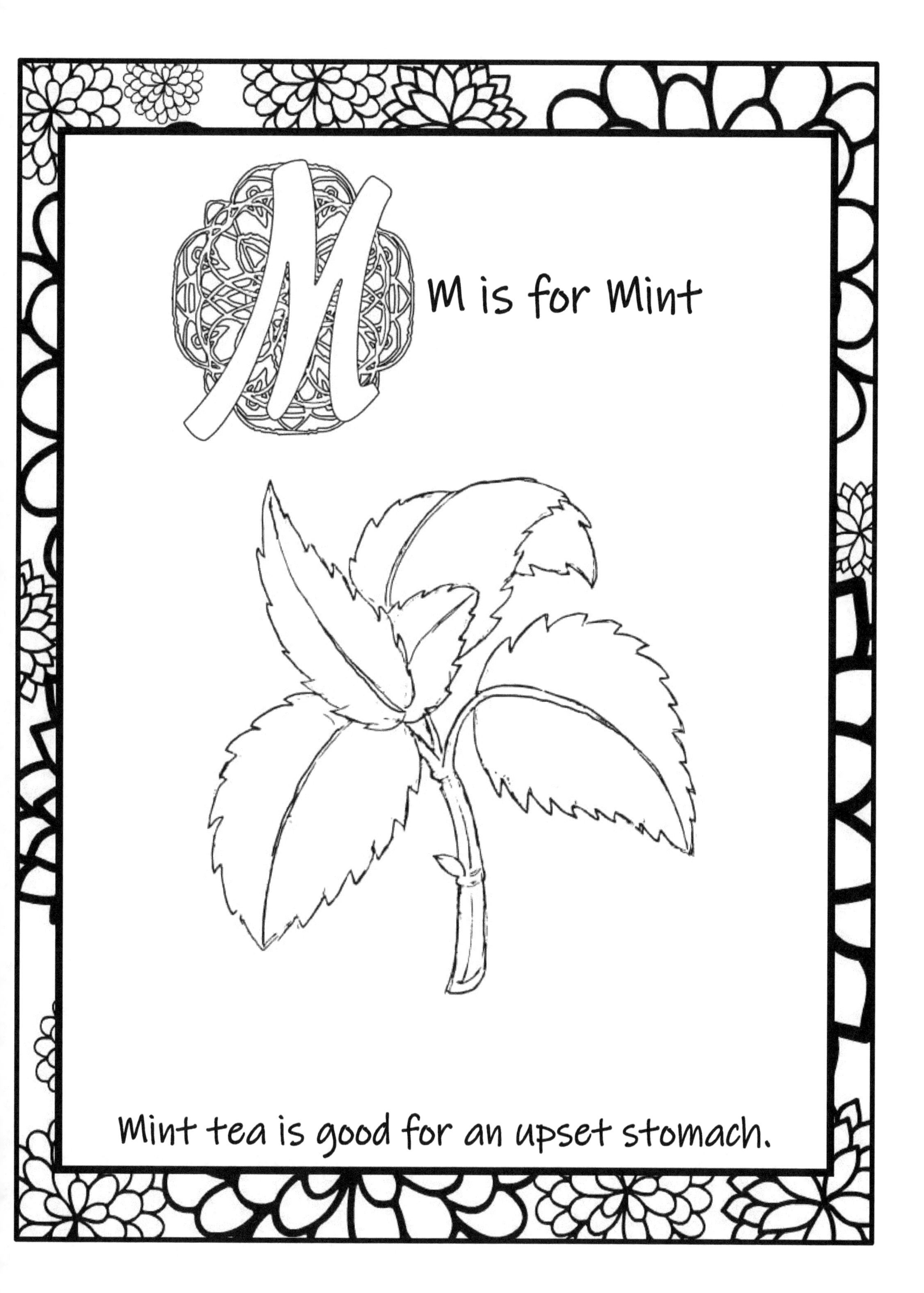
M is for Mint
Mint tea is good for an upset stomach.

N is for Nutmeg

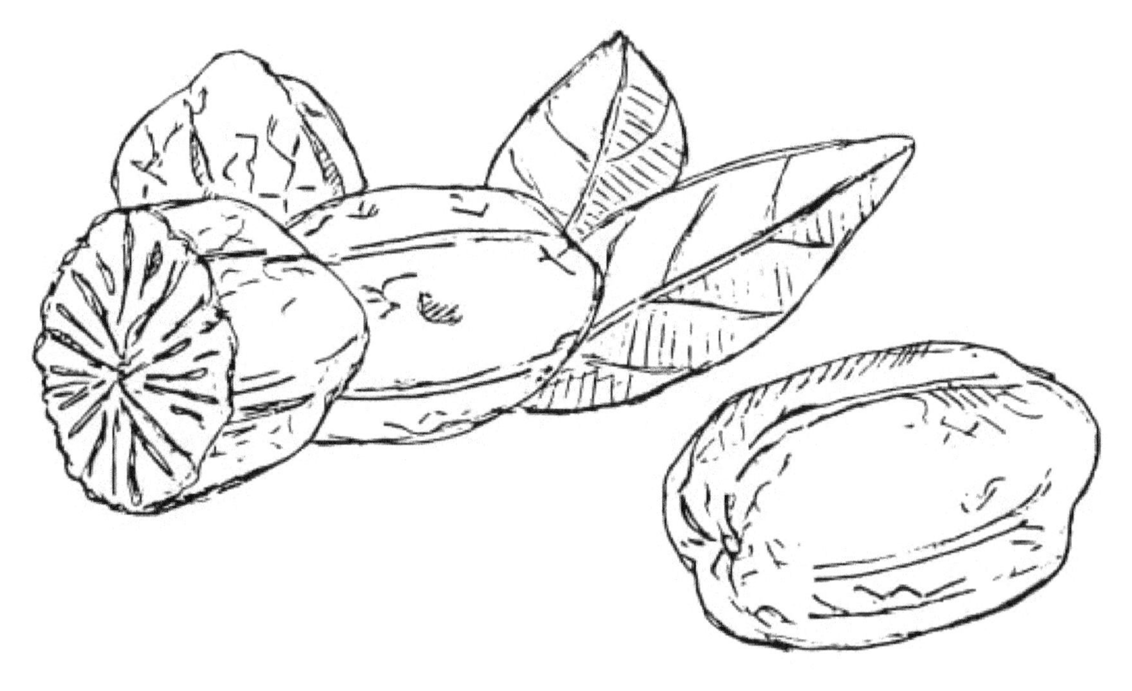

Nutmeg may help with sleeping.

O is for Olive Leaf
Olive Leaf can help your immune system if you are sick.

P is for Parsley

Parsley is great in food and has Vitamins A, B, C, and E in it.

Q is for Dong Quai
Dong Quai is a great herb for women. It's
also good for energy and blood circulation.

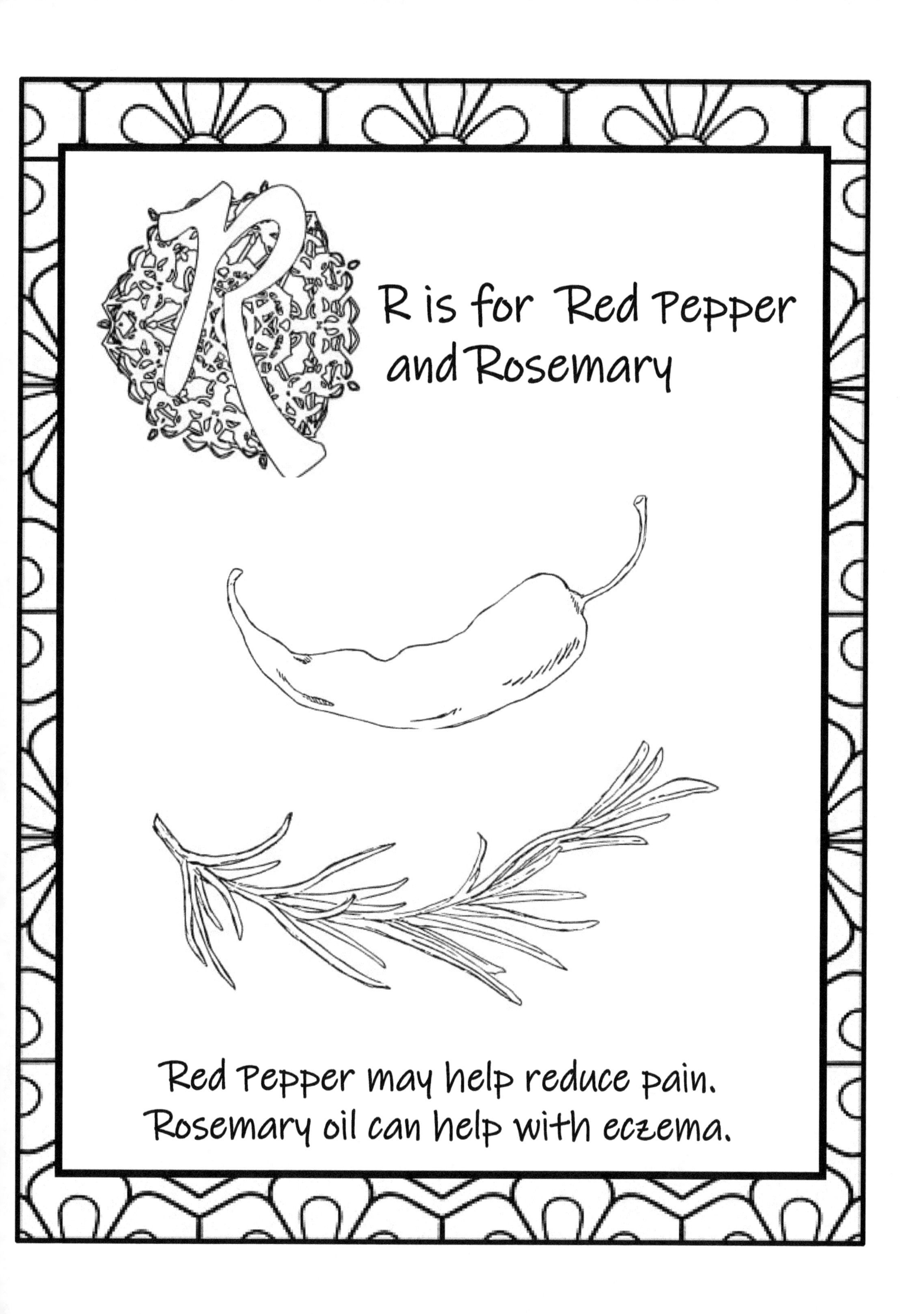
R is for Red Pepper
and Rosemary
Red Pepper may help reduce pain.
Rosemary oil can help with eczema.

S is for Sage and Sesame
Sage has many health benefits
and may help with memory.
Sesame seeds may be good for your heart.

T is for Tamarind,
Thyme, and Turmeric
Tamarind can be used to help diarrhea.
Thyme can help fight cold symptoms.
Turmeric has many health benefits. It has many
minerals and may help your liver and digestion.

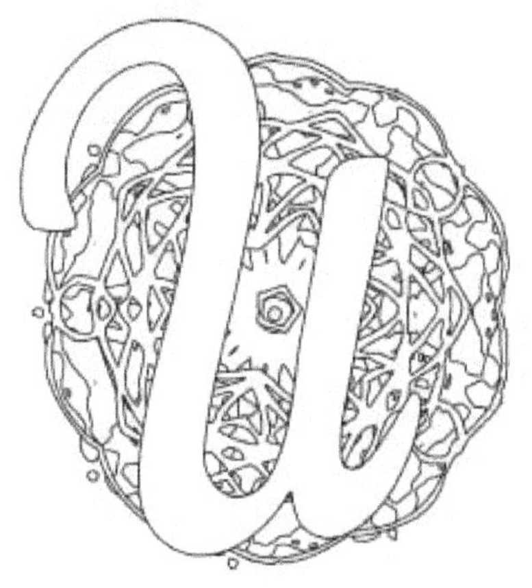

U is for Uva Ursi

Uva Ursi can help with bladder and kidney infections.

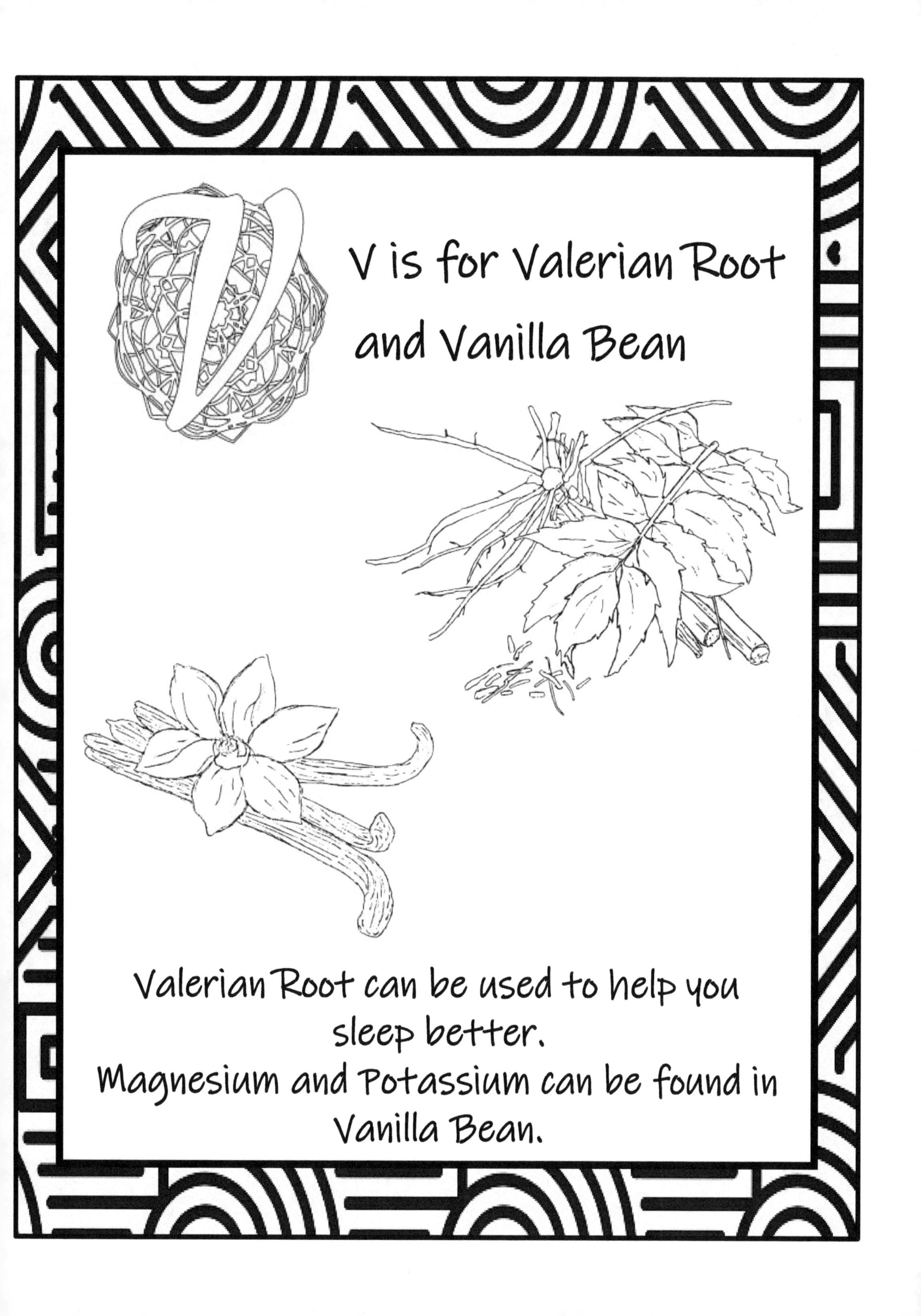
V is for Valerian Root
and Vanilla Bean
Valerian Root can be used to help you
sleep better.
Magnesium and Potassium can be found in
Vanilla Bean.

W is for Witch Hazel
Witch Hazel can help with itching.

X is for Xantham Gum

Xanthan Gum can help control blood sugar for people with type 2 diabetes.

Y is for Young Hyson
Young Hyson can help if you have a toothache.

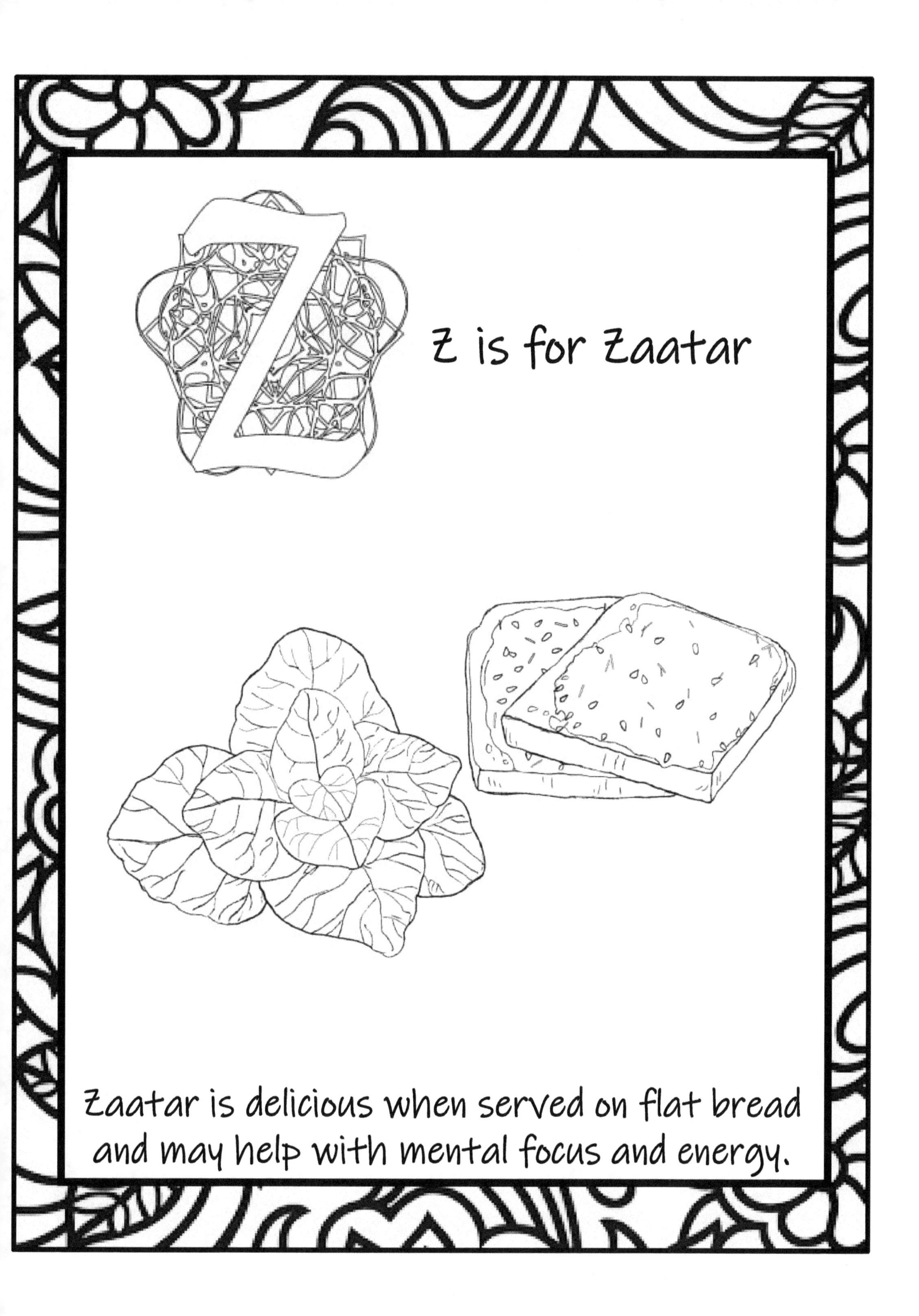
Z
Z is for Zaatar
Zaatar is delicious when served on flat bread
and may help with mental focus and energy.

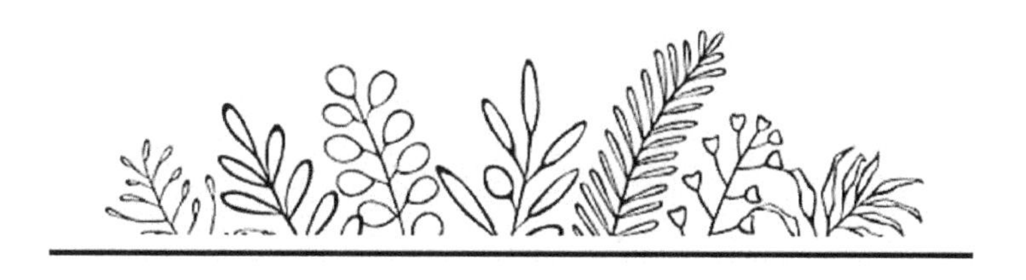

Let's Connect!!!

For more fun and interactive info about

Herbs and Spices

and many other topics:

Join us on Social Media (Facebook and Instagram):

@ScienceCreations

View our YouTube Channel:

YouTube.com search "Science Creations"

And visit our Website:

www.ScienceCreations.com

Direct message us with your colored-in pages for a chance to be featured online!

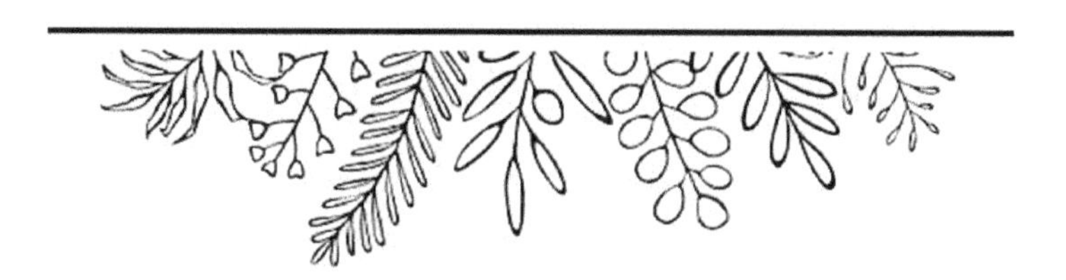

Printed in the USA
CPSIA information can be obtained
at www.ICGtesting.com
LVHW071808130224
771621LV00039B/549